Dinosaurs!
Sticker Book

Contents

Here Comes Mr Dinosaur!

Peppa and George are playing a new game. They're pretending that their bedroom is the land of the dinosaurs! George is in charge of Mr Dinosaur. Grrr! Stick in some more toys. Can you add some friends to join in the game?

Into the Museum

The museum is full of interesting things. Peppa and George are looking around the dinosaur room with Mummy and Daddy Pig. What's waiting for them in here? Fill the room with amazing dinosaur models and the dinosaur robot.

Big Bones

Now George wants to see a real dinosaur. Real dinosaurs are very, very old. Mr Rabbit is in charge of the old things at the museum. This dinosaur skeleton is even older than he is! Stick in the dinosaur skeleton's missing bones, then add Peppa, George and some more visitors.

Grampy Rabbit's Adventure

Grampy Rabbit likes dinosaurs, too. He has made up an adventure about a lost jungle world! Add some brave explorers crawling through this dinosaur's legs. Can you hide the explorers so that the dinosaur won't see them?

Dinosaur Explorers

Peppa and George love pretending to be explorers. They are on an adventure in the rainforest, searching for dinosaurs. Stick in Peppa and George in their explorer outfits and add dinosaurs and other creatures, too. How many dinosaurs have they spotted?

Dinosaur Park

The dinosaur park is open. Peppa and George can't wait to go inside. Who else is visiting the dinosaur park today? Use your stickers to decide! Can you add some pretend dinosaurs, popping up to say hello?

The Ginormous Slide

Edmond Elephant has found a ginormous slide. It looks just like a dinosaur! Edmond says that the slide is an Apatosaurus. Edmond knows a lot about dinosaurs. He is a clever clogs. Stick in Peppa and George's friends sliding down the dinosaur's neck. Wheeeeeee!

New Clothes

Peppa, Suzy, George and Richard are taking their toys to Miss Rabbit's shop to buy them some new clothes. Stick all the outfits on the hangers. What sort of outfit would suit Mr Dinosaur? Dress him up, then choose an outfit for Richard's favourite dinosaur, too.

Once Upon a Dinosaur

Shh! Everyone has to be quiet in the library. Granny and Grandpa Pig have brought George to find some books in the children's section. George wants to find a book about a dinosaur! Stick in lots of stories . . . and lots of happy readers!

Dinosaur Egg

Peppa's playgroup are going on a nature walk. They are looking for insects and leaves and other little things. Freddy Fox has found a BIG thing. It is a dinosaur egg! Madame Gazelle will be very surprised! Stick her in, then add the giant egg.

Bouncy Castle

It's George's birthday today. Mummy and Daddy Pig have got him a treat - a bouncy castle in the shape of a dinosaur! Miss Rabbit has also brought some balloons to George's party. Can you guess what birthday balloon George would like? Stick a balloon on each of the strings and add George's friends bouncing on the dinosaur's back, too. Hip hip hooray!

When I Grow Up

When George grows up, he wants to be a fossil expert in a dinosaur-research team. George is at the beach with Edmond and Richard, hunting for fossils. Add them in their archaeologist outfits. Can you help them discover buried fossils? Stick some into the sand.